Ted drove the
red party bus.

Ted stopped at Jack's house.

"Whose party is it?" asked Ted.

6

"Wait and see," said Jack's mum.

8

Then Ted picked up Sam,

and Kate,

and Anna,

and Mohammed.

11

"Whose party are we going to?" asked Ted.

"Don't you know?"
the children said.

Ted picked up Ben,
Dan and Jess.

"But whose party is it?" asked Ted.

"You'll see!"
they all said.

17

"Stop here," said Jack's mum.

"But that's my house!"
said Ted.

"It's your party, Ted!"

20

21

Puzzle Time!

Put these pictures in the right order and retell the story!

curious

happy

puzzled

excited

Which words describe Ted and which describe the children?

 Turn over for answers!

Notes for adults

TADPOLES are structured to provide support for newly independent readers. The stories may also be used by adults for sharing with young children.

Starting to read alone can be daunting. **TADPOLES** help by providing visual support and repeating words and phrases. These books will both develop confidence and encourage reading and rereading for pleasure.

If you are reading this book with a child, here are a few suggestions:

1. Make reading fun! Choose a time to read when you and the child are relaxed and have time to share the story.
2. Talk about the story before you start reading. Look at the cover and the blurb. What might the story be about? Why might the child like it?
3. Encourage the child to retell the story, using the jumbled picture puzzle as a starting point. Extend vocabulary with the matching words to characters puzzle.
4. Discuss the story and see if the child can relate it to their own experience.
5. Give praise! Remember that small mistakes need not always be corrected.

Answers

Here is the correct order:

1.e   2.a   3. f   4.d   5.c   6.b

Words to describe Ted:
curious, puzzled
Words to describe
the children:
excited, happy